3.70

123

AND

THINGS

First published 1976 by Ernest Benn Limited

Picturemac edition published 1993

This edition first published 1989 by Pan Macmillan Children's Books
a division of Pan Macmillan Publishers Limited
Cavaye Place London SW10 9PG
and Basingstoke

Associated companies throughout the world

ISBN 0-333-56072-8

Copyright © 1976 Colin McNaughton

1 3 5 7 9 8 6 4 2

A CIP catalogue record for this book is available from
the British Library

Printed in Hong Kong

Colin McNaughton's

123 AND THINGS

PAN MACMILLAN CHILDREN'S BOOKS

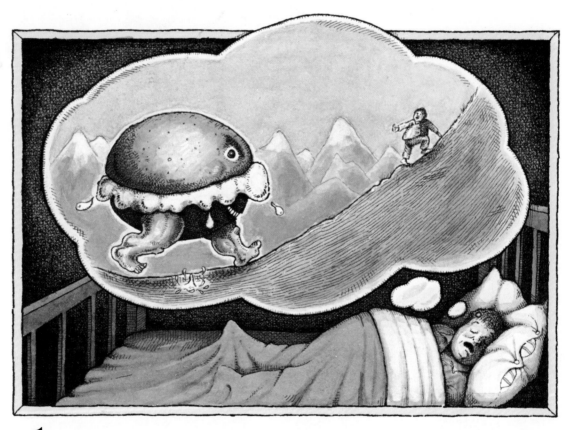

1 One on the run from a vast cream bun

2   Two marabou say how do you do

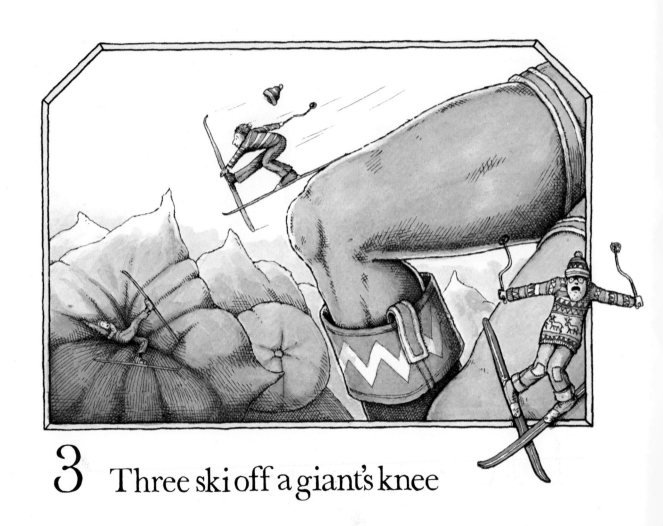

3 Three ski off a giant's knee

4 Four in awe of a dinosaur

5 Five on a drive - will they survive?

6 Six do tricks on candlesticks

7 Seven in heaven in deepest Devon

8 Eight, late, await their fate

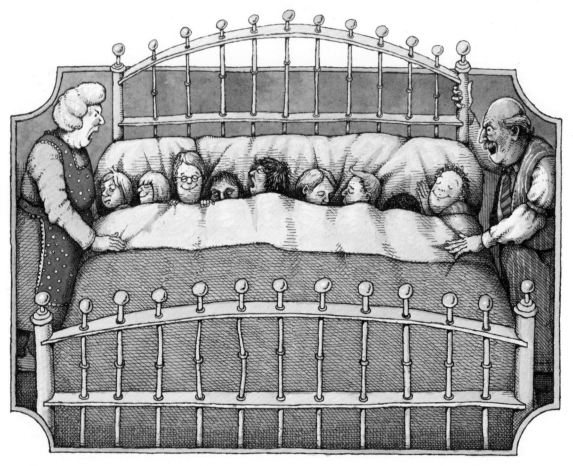

9   Nine decline to rise and shine

10 Ten young men in a lion's den

11 Eleven bears without any cares

12 Twelve baboons in blue balloons

13 Thirteen rats in old men's hats

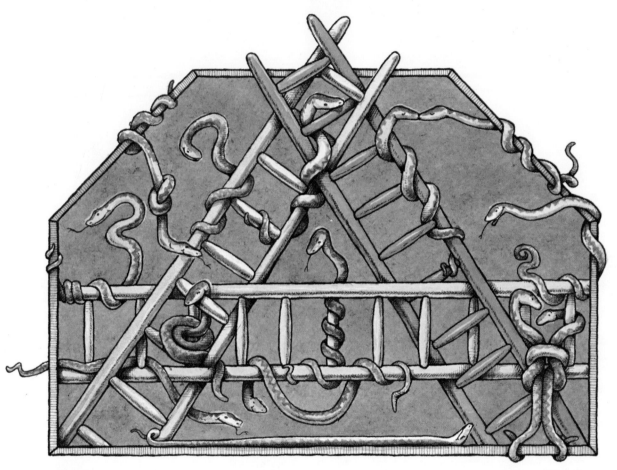

14 Fourteen adders play snakes and ladders

15 Fifteen boys make a monstrous noise

16 Sixteen birds say absurd words

17 Seventeen pigs in various wigs

18 Eighteen fly from a hot mince pie

19 Nineteen girls all diving for pearls

20 Twenty climb for the very first time

50,084 Fifty thousand and eighty four

could not believe just what they saw